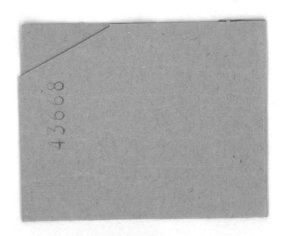

THE WORLD
THROUGH THE WINDOW

Collected Poems for Children

ROY FULLER

THE WORLD THROUGH THE WINDOW

Collected Poems for Children

Illustrated by Nick Duffy

BLACKIE

Copyright © 1972, 1977, 1982 and 1989 Roy Fuller
Illustrations © 1989 Nick Duffy
First published 1989 by Blackie and Son Ltd

British Library Cataloguing in Publication Data
Fuller, Roy, *1912–*
    The world through the window
    I. Title   II. Duffy, Nick
    821'.912
    ISBN 0 216 92659 9

Blackie and Son Ltd
7 Leicester Place
London WC2H 7BP

Printed in Great Britain

Author's Note

This volume includes the poems in two previous books of my verse for children, now out of print, *Seen Grandpa Lately?* and *Poor Roy*. Thanks to the goodwill of the Oxford University Press it also includes my poems in *Upright Downfall*, a collection of three poets' work. I have added a few more recent and previously uncollected poems.

Bringing Up Babies

If babies could speak they'd tell mother or nurse
That slapping was pointless, and why:
For if you're not crying it prompts you to cry,
And if you are – then you cry worse.

The National Union of Children

NUC has just passed a weighty resolution:
'Unless all parents raise our rate of pay
This action will be taken by our members
(The resolution comes in force today):-

'Noses will not be blown (sniffs are in order),
Bedtime will get preposterously late,
Ice-cream and crisps will be consumed for
    breakfast,
Unwanted cabbage left upon the plate,

'Earholes and finger-nails can't be inspected,
Overtime (known as homework) won't be
    worked,
Reports from school will all say "Could do better",
Putting bricks back in boxes may be shirked.'

The National Association of Parents

Of course, NAP's answer quickly was forthcoming
(It was a matter of emergency),
It issued to the Press the following statement
(Its Secretary appeared upon TV):-

'True that the so-called Saturday allowance
Hasn't kept pace with prices in the shops,
But neither have, alas, parental wages:
NUC's claim would ruin kind, hard-working Pops.

'Therefore, unless that claim is now abandoned,
Strike action for us, too, is what remains;
In planning for the which we are in process
Of issuing, to all our members, canes.'

TV

In the coloured world of home
there's a greyish oblong hole;
and it's the only thing that
moves among the furniture.

Somewhere past the couch tiny
clouds and horses spring into
view and disappear before
they get to the window-sill.

Though these things and beings are
so small, their noise is human.
Passing empty rooms, you hear
gun-shots and angry talking.

Even when there is no one
to see or hear it, this life
in the curved glass probably
goes on just the same. Who knows?

Our universe began in
a concentrated atom.
So does this screen of shadows
when you first switch on the knob.

It also ends like that as
you switch the other way, though
first the sound dies, and all yell,
but cannot make themselves heard.

POSTCRIPT: ON THE ARRIVAL OF COLOUR

In the greyish world of home
there's a coloured oblong hole;
and naturally we all sit
with our red eyes glued on it.

Girl Making Pies

When my mother's making pies
I usually make one, too.
Mine is always midget size
And it never seems to rise.

Mother's pies are very tasty
And yet whatever I do
Mine are almost only pastry:
You could nearly call them nasty.

Into hers you couldn't cram
More stuff or else they'd burst:
In mine there's just a hint of lamb,
One currant or a vein of jam.

But Dad must like them best, because
He eats the grey things first;
For once not saying, as he gnaws:
'Go and wash those filthy paws.'

Horrible Things

'What's the horriblest thing you've seen?'
Said Nell to Jean.

'Some grey-coloured, trodden-on plasticine;
On a plate, a left-over cold baked bean;
A cloak-room ticket numbered thirteen;
A slice of meat without any lean;
The smile of a spiteful fairy-tale queen;
A thing in the sea like a brown submarine;
A cheese fur-coated in brilliant green;
A bluebottle perched on a piece of sardine.
What's the horriblest thing *you've* seen?'
Said Jean to Nell.

'Your face, as you tell
Of all the horriblest things you've seen.'

Teresa Nude

Teresa bathing, glancing down, said: 'Mummy,
I wonder what it looks like in my tummy.'

The answer: pictures in a range of inks
From deepest scarlet to indifferent pinks.

– Though possibly the liver, some would deem,
Being purplish-brown, outside this colour-scheme.

And pale the bowels' wrinkled furbelows,
Packaged as neatly as a brand-new hose.

Though in the 'tummy' scarcely to be placed,
The fiery lung-trees grow up from the waist.

And a few miscellaneous parts propel
Juices and dinners through the hues of hell.

Teresa, thanks for acting as our guide
To all the beauteous sights we have inside.

Yet better we should merely show our skin,
Be made not inside out but inside in –

For how could we be ever calmly viewed
If the above were what we looked like nude?

Cherry Time

Where Chloë has been sitting lie
Scatterings of humeri
From petite and green-boned peoples;
And as many shrunken skulls.
I wonder she could bear to sit
So long in that burial pit.

Drawing

Small boys and girls can draw a house
But find it hard to draw a mouse.

Most drawing in a house is square:
Square walls and windows in square air.

– Though from the chimneys, I don't doubt,
Nothing square can ever come out.

But smoke is really only scribble:
Not so the beast that loves to nibble.

You'd need a film to show a nose
That always quivers as it goes.

Even invisible ink wouldn't meet
The problem of tiny rapid feet.

If you were colouring the fur –
Grey or brown, which would you prefer?

And were you getting down the tail
And put a corner in, you'd fail.

And how to show those long front teeth,
The bottom lip tucked underneath;

The upper ditto very bristly?
Your style would have to be quite Whistlery.

Besides, a mouse would never keep still
Long enough to let you draw it well.

And were one brought in by the cat
You'd be too sad to copy that.

Strange that a mixture of curves and hair
Likes living in a thing so square:

It could, were it self-advertising,
Make life and art much more surprising.

A Boy's Clothes

In bed I see my clothes
Over the chair and floor,
And wonder at the shape
That they were tailored for.

Bent on a wizened chest,
Two handless arms repose;
The legs are short and wide,
The severed feet lack toes.

Though when I go downstairs
No one cries out in fright:
Apparently I manage
To make the things look right.

But thickness must seem strange
To that creature by the bed;
My movements ghostly and
Superfluous my head.

A Boy's Friend

I have a secret friend
With whom I never quarrel.
I'm Watson to his Holmes,
He's Hardy to my Laurel.

I'm greedy for his calls
And leave him with sad heart.
He thinks of marvellous games.
He mends what comes apart.

Though when he isn't here
I can't recall his face,
I'm always glancing at
That slightly freckled space.

His name's quite ordinary
But seems unusual.
His brain's stocked like a shop.
His talk is comical.

Often with other friends
Play ends in biffs and screams:
With him, play calmly goes
Through dusk – and even dreams.

Child Wondering

I wonder what I used to be
Before I started out as me.
I remember crawling on the floor
But hardly anything before.
Yet sometimes waking in the dark
I see a little turning spark
As though another world had once
Impressed itself upon my glance;
And hear a train I never hear
In daytime anywhere so near;
And think that in the whole of space
To be in bed's the oddest place,
Forgetting quite how safe it seemed
Before I fell asleep and dreamed.

When morning comes and sunlight falls
On maps and faces on the walls,
And birds are saying what can be
Hummed but not understood by me;
And reading in my bedside books
Of pies made out of singing rooks,
And the complaints by nervous bears
Of girls whose bottoms dint their chairs –
Gradually I start to feel
The realness of the strangely real;
And by the time I cut my bacon
Know that I'm probably mistaken
To think it's any use to wonder
What lies behind, in front, out yonder.

Ermyntrude

A little girl named Ermyntrude
Was often curiously rude –
Came down to breakfast in the nude.
Her sister said (though not a prude):
'It seems to me extremely crude
To see your tummy over food:
Your conduct borders on the lewd.
Also, you nastily exude
Cornflakes and milk as though you'd spewed' –
Her lips were open when she chewed,
And read a comic-book called *Dude*.
She was a sight not to be viewed
Without profound disquietude.
Though what could come but such a mood
From anyone named Ermyntrude?

The Start of a Memorable Holiday

Good evening, sir. Good evening, ma'am. Good
  evening, little ladies.
From all the staff, a hearty welcome to the Hotel
  Hades.
Oh yes, sir, since you booked your rooms we have
  been taken over
And changed our name – but for the better – as
  you'll soon discover.
Porter, Room 99! Don't worry, sir – just now he
  took
Much bulkier things than bags on his pathetic iron
  hook.
The other room, the children's room? I'm very
  pleased to say
We've put them in the annexe, half a mile across
  the way.
They'll have a nearer view there of the bats'
  intriguing flying,
And you, dear sir and madam, won't be troubled
  by their crying
– Although I'm sure that neither of them's
  frightened of the gloom.
Besides, the maid will try to find a candle for their
  room.
Of course, ma'am, we've a maid there, she's the
  porter's (seventh) wife:
She'll care for these dear children quite as well as
  her own life.

The journey's tired them? Ah, tonight they won't
be counting sheep!

I'll see they have a nice hot drink before they're
put to sleep.

Don't be too late yourselves, sir, for the hotel's
evening meal:

I hope that on the menu will be some roast milk-
fed veal.

If you'll forgive me, I must stoke the ovens right
away:

It's going to be (excuse the joke) hell in this place
today!

Yes, I do all the cooking *and* the getting of the
meat:

Though we're so far from shops we've usually
something fresh to eat.

Of course, it isn't always veal, and when the
school terms start

Joints may get tougher. But our gravy still stays
full of heart!

In the Restaurant

Said the waiter to the bald man:
'Have you studied the bill of fare?'
Said the bald man to the waiter:
'I'd like a portion of hare.'

His wife said: 'Were you choosing,
What would you choose?' said she.
'Not corn on the cob,' said the waiter.
'My own corn's killing me.'

Their guest, puzzling over the menu,
Said: 'I'll have the Angus Game.'
'I'm sorry, sir,' said the waiter,
'That's the proprietor's name.'

Said a man at the next table
In a voice like a bell's deep toll
(He was wearing a clerical collar):
'Don't overlook the sole.'

'I'm very fond of Stilton,
Cheddar and Brie, so please,'
Said a little chap in the corner,
'I'd like some of your lychees.'

A table for six in the middle
Had to seat a crowd of fourteen.
Said they, when they ordered their starters:
'We all rather feel like sardines.'

A Red Indian came through the doorway
(His squaw shouldered their papoose).
'I've been hunting all day,' he shouted,
'And I want an extra large mousse.'

– Followed by an actor, saying
In tones deliberately droll
(He was 'resting' at the moment):
'And *I* want a nice big roll.'

Said the proprietor to the waiter:
'These customers make me ill.
Give them all duck or turkey,
And don't forget the bill.'

Australia

Quite obviously in Australia
Everything's upside down;
And you must be an absolute failure
If you happen to wear a crown.

Do you walk, to get through a door,
On the ceiling? Does a bird
Perch out of harm on the floor?
Is 'top' a rather rude word?

Is headball played, and elevennis?
If you hate anyone is it love?
Of course, they don't know where heaven is
Except that it's not up above.

Are holidays longer than terms?
Are humbugs good for you?
No doubt deep in the sky are worms,
And served first is the last in the queue.

Do dogs sniff each others' noses
And wag them when they are glad?
Are dandelions not roses
Carefully grown by Dad?

Do children go to the office?
Does Mother tell awful lies?
And Grandpa buy comics and toffees,
Gran's skirt give her chilly thighs?

If so, I'll not go to Australia,
Where at jokes a listener sobs.
Besides, I prefer a dahlia
To grow flowers rather than knobs.

Epitaphs

Here lies a careless boy named Gunn
Who fed a lion with a bun.
At least, in one hand held a bun
But, typically, fed the other one.

A man called Percy Brown lies here
Who used to sip his father's beer.
And later on he sipped his own:
His weight at death was forty stone.

Here lies a greedy girl, Jane Bevan,
Whose breakfasts hardly ever stopped.
One morning at half past eleven
She snapped and crackled and then popped.

A schoolmistress called Binks lies here.
She held her own for twenty year.
She pleaded, biffed, said: 'I'm your friend.'
But children got her in the end.

Here lies Prue Jones, whose childish folly
Was to eat too much of a lime iced lolly
And get a splinter in a place
Where splinters make a hopeless case.

Here lies John Smith, exactly eight,
Who was given a handsome chemistry set.
Here also lies his sister, Maria.
Or what was left of them after the fire.

Here lies Amanda Mary Wilde
Who was in fact a lying child.
Her end came as she told a whopper
While sucking a two-penny gob-stopper.

Here lies a family dog called Rover:
His pampered life at last is over.
On Rover more than on each other
Love was bestowed by Dad and Mother.

Here lies a precocious, insomniac tot
Who knew how to let down the side of his cot.
He undid the catches one evening at seven
And, the bars having vanished, fell straight up to
    heaven.

Stables' Tables

There was a girl called Sheila Stables
Who never really knew her tables.
At least, with study she was able
To get to know the twice times table;
Then having had revealed the trick,
She learned her ten times fairly quick.
A friend of hers called Mabel Gimpel
Said five and eleven were just as simple,
But Sheila never found this so.
Particularly hard to know
Were nine and seven times. Miss Bass
(Who took the mathematics class)
Would call out: 'Sheila Stables, what
Are seven nines? . . . Oh, no, they're not.'

Her bad marks in this subject rather
Worried her. She told her father,
Who laughed and said: 'Why goodness me,
There are more vital matters, She,
Than learning boring things by heart –
For instance, human love, and art.'
A poetic man was Mr Stables
Who'd never quite got right *his* tables
And if required to do a sum
Would use four fingers and a thumb.

'What's nine times seven?' asked Miss Bass.
'Only, my father says, an ass
Would know the answer,' Sheila said,
Though not without a sense of dread.
'I asked you, not your father,' Miss
Bass cried. 'Nought out of ten for this.'

Whether in later life She Stables
Had ever mastered all her tables
I do not know, but she became

A greater player of the game
Than even the formidable Bass.
She worked out when the sun would pass
Behind the planet Minotaur
(A body quite unknown before
The book of astronomic tables
Compiled by Dr Sheila Stables);
And put, the right way up, a bit
Of puzzle Einstein failed to fit.
It seemed the world did not depend
On having at one's fingers' end
Nine eights or seven sixes – though
Poetry itself could never show
(As Sheila was the first to say)
The Past, the Purpose and the Way:
And somewhere midst the curious laws
Enacted by the Primal Cause
There enters (usually in the heavens)
Such things as nine, or seven, sevens.

Advice to Poets

If you lack an inventive brain
Writing a poem is hell.
Choose a form that has a refrain,

Then the subsequent stanzas' strain
You'll be able to bear fairly well.
If you lack an inventive brain

Before (as I'm trying to explain)
Even starting your doggerel
Choose a form that has a refrain.

Forms help to keep poets sane
(A good one's the villanelle
If you lack an inventive brain),

For most poets compose with pain
And this tip will some pain dispel –
Choose a form that has a refrain.

Get one line or, preferably, twain;
Go on ringing them like a bell:
If you lack an inventive brain
Choose a form. That has a refrain.

The Poets

Though Shakespeare's our national bard
His poetry's terribly hard.
It would benefit those
Who were sitting their 'O's
If in *Lear* it was Noddy who starred.

In the muscular verse of John Donne
There's not a great deal of clean fun;
So until you're on terms
With women or worms
He's one of the poets to shun.

Would he ever have stayed at the Hilton,
That Puritan poet called Milton?
Of course the polemic
Is quite academic –
In *his* day Park Lane wasn't built on.

In the era of Dryden and Pope
Poets didn't write adverts for soap.
They earned their reward
By soft-soaping some lord,
And washed with cold water and hope.

What else may be said against Blake
He certainly wasn't a fake.
Some poems were mad,
Many more very bad,
But a few make the reader's voice shake.

The Scot loves the poems of Burns
Save some he high-mindedly spurns:
Though oddly enough
That rather rude stuff
Is just what the Englishman learns.

To find if a man is scoundrelly
Ask: 'Do you like Keats more than Shelley?'
This test you can do
On but one or two,
Since these poets aren't featured on telly.

A poem addressed to Lord Tennyson
Has got to avoid the rhyme 'venison'
Which sounds quite obscene
Close to one whom the Queen
Endowed with her personal benison.

Some people say 'W. B. Yeats'
To rhyme with another bard, Keats.
The fault is not great
Since mere mention of Yeats
Puts a speaker among the aesthetes.

The Poet

The heron is more than a hero,
While the starling is only a stare:
And though one is bigger than zero
It looks rather lean when it's bare.

Why do I write down such stanzas?
It's not that I'm cracked or jocose,
But some think mad extravaganzas
Guarantee that they're not reading prose.

The Minstrel

I came into the hall
Out of the biting squall:
The snow lay on my shoulders like a shawl.

I heard the monarch call,
Raising his goblet tall,
For a tale to hold the company in thrall –

That told of some great fall
And nicely would appall
Those safely sheltered from the weather's brawl.

I saw fissures in the wall
And things that freely crawl
Over the stones of Egypt, Carthage, Gaul;

And then began to bawl
The tale told by us all,
That starts thuswise: 'I came into the hall . . .'

After the Poetry-reading

In the room of the poetry-reading
When the poetry-reading was done,
The poets and their admirers
Met for coffee and a bun.

A few had bought books of poems
Which the poets were asked to sign:
Thinking of their percentage,
They signed on the dotted line.

Talking to elderly ladies,
Their eyes on the girls in the throng,
They wondered if this were the purpose
Of growing their hair so long.

Names

Before I was christened my grandfather said
That what they proposed to call me – Roy –
Was the name of a big black dog, not a boy;
And he knew about names because his was Fred.

Suppose you could choose, what name would
    you pick?
Almost certainly never the name you've got.
But the trouble is, that though you think you're not,
You really are Cyril or Sydney or Dick.

And only in tales is the hero called
Peregrine, Lancelot or Captain Blood:
The man who does deeds of actual good
Is usually something like Archibald.

And so the lesson seems perfectly plain:
You can make a name, not the name make you.
And big black dogs need not form the view
That I took their name entirely in vain.

To my Grand-daughter, Learning the Flute

Many can play on the flute
With lips that are fat or hirsute.
So those who possess perfect bows
Will flute them to shame, I suppose.
And since elegant Handel sonatas
Emerge through moustached split tomatoes,
From cherries there may well be blown
Forms of beauty so far unknown.
The gadget itself, come to think,
Started out as the virtuous Syrinx.

Bees in August

It's rather unfair they should not only smell
But gobble the lavender blossom as well.

Autumn

Sweeping up leaves, I come
across a few dead blooms
I just don't remember
growing in summer – queer
pink-striped stalks; and some
purple cone shapes – mushrooms?
'Last week's Fifth November,'
I think, and all is clear.

After Breakfast

I stop myself sliding a morsel
Of bacon fat into the bin.
It will make a whole meal for the robin,
His legs are so terribly thin.

The Retired Man Goes Shopping

In the middle of the morning I often go out,
Passing pensioners pushing their baskets on
    wheels,
And babies in strollers by mothers in rollers
Who seem far too young for the job, one feels.
I'm seen as a pensioner, too, without doubt,
But I'm not yet so ancient or daft to be willing
To purchase such things as 'battered fish fingers'
Or (as the butcher prints) 'LEAN BREASTS ONE
    SHILLING'.

The 4 a.m. Bluebottle

The fly was peacefully sleeping,
No doubt, till I turned on the light.
Now it alternates between creeping
On my nose and lunatic flight.

Shall I switch back to the gloaming
That makes insomnia worse,
Or try to put up with this roaming
That distracts me from writing verse?

I must admit I mull over
A squirt of insecticide,
But whether for me or the rover
I can't really quite decide.

Song

I like to think the thrushes sing to me:
I copy phrases of the song they know.
If they're not very far up in the tree,
Sometimes I see them cock their heads – as
   though

They recognised my all too human art;
As though my being near them changed the song;
As though their lives were influenced in part
By what I may have uttered in their tongue.

But even through my absence in the house
The song goes on; and then, to catch the falling
Sun, the bird climbs to higher and higher boughs,
Until the trembling throat's invisibly calling.

– Like poets singing; and how everyone
Feels he makes contact with those moving on.

Starlings

The starlings at the garden bowl
Remind me of children round a pool.
They don't allow each other in;
They hesitate upon the brink;
They all keep up a squawking din;
They make the water feculent.

However, children do not drink
Bathwater save by accident.

Snow

Snow falling in November
May fall on a yellow rose,
Forming an ice-cream cornet
That with ice-cream overflows.

When snow falls in December
It has only a bare black twig
To chalk on a sky of yellow
And make unusually big.

If snow should fall in April
How hard to tell its crumb
From petals cast in the border
Or blossom on the plum.

Nature

In their nest the birds arrange
Abstract shapes of four or five.
Do they find it very strange
Soon to see there something live?

Azure ovals, speckled brown,
Changed to bits of naked skin –
Then, relief when mouth of clown
Turns to beak's sardonic grin?

No strangeness nor relief is there:
Nature accepts what nature works.
It's only we who seek and bear
Meanings where no meaning lurks.

At the Garden Bowl Again

Sparrows aren't very great bathers
Though they like a dip in the dust,
But starlings queue up for the water –
Then seem able only to just
Take off with a water-logged thrust.

Pigeons can siphon the liquid
Without ever raising their beaks;
Other birds appear to be gargling
As they scoop up a billful that leaks.
But pigeons are usually freaks.

So I sit with my whisky and soda,
Observing these species of fowl,
And they in their turn watch me closely
To see if I throw back my jowl
Or suck from my own garden bowl.

Note

After writing the above poem I came to realise I was wrong about
sparrows. Gilbert White put the true position just about 200 years
ago in *The Natural History of Selbourne*: 'As far as I can observe, many
birds that dust themselves never wash: and I once thought that
those birds that wash themselves would never dust; but here I find
myself mistaken; for common house-sparrows are great pulvera-
trices, being frequently seen grovelling and wallowing in dusty
roads; and yet they are great washers.'

The World Through the Window

Sometimes birds fly against the glass
Towards the boughs reflected there,
Thinking they are about to pass
Into a forest, strange and rare.

Fruits darkly glisten on each tree,
Unpierced by any other bill.
The vision stuns: occasionally,
Is even liable to kill.

It's like what we ourselves may see
The other side of that same glass –
A fire; a favourite face, settee;
Set out against the evening grass.

Below the sill our eyes alight
Upon the bird that visualised
Another world. Its eyes are tight;
Its beak is open, dumb, surprised.

Take-over by the Garden

In the end, the garden creatures became more
    friendly.
The ladybird led by refusing to fly from our finger –
More than usually – fluffing her wings out from
    their cases
Then putting them very neatly back again.

The blackbird didn't stop at the threshold, but
    showed
The bald rings round his eyes, his earth-crumbed
    bill,
His white chinks in his glossy armour of black,
Among the curving chair-legs and our slippers.

And the dusty bristles of the hedgehog made
Our sofas difficult to lie on: bees
Drank with us at our bedside tumblers of water:
In the bath, living frogs as well as plastic dolphins.

And no one seemed to quarrel in front of the owl,
Standing at the end of the shelf like a
    loudspeaker.
Our lives were full of little important cares;
And happily this happened all the world over.

The Dream

There was a dream that kept recurring:
It seemed absurd to dream that dream
In such a place, at such sad time.

Who would have known of the recurring
But for the broken stones that lean
Where parliaments of men have been? –

That in a way were like the dream,
Though falling short of its great scheme;
That were more like the dream's recurring.

Advice to Children

1
Caterpillars living on lettuce
Are the colour of their host:
Look out, when you're eating a salad,
For the greens that move the most.

Close your mouth tight when you're running
As when washing you shut your eyes,
Then as soap is kept from smarting
So will tonsils be from flies.

If in spite of such precautions
Anything nasty gets within,
Remember it will be thinking:
'Far worse for me than him.'

2
If in the middle of the night
Your bedside water tastes of cloth,
It means that possibly you might
By accident have drunk a moth.

In summer it's as well you should
Switch on the light before you sip,
For others actually could
Be taking then their midnight dip.

3

Plate-glass doors form a dangerous duo:
Never, when using them, try
To enter the place by the one marked TUO
Or withdraw through the one marked ИI.

4

The world is dark with rumours
And things may happen to you.
Keep your handkerchief in your bloomers
And your money in your shoe.

The Courts

I always think the Diamond dynasty
A trifle sinister. The King displays
Only one eye: perhaps the other's patched.
The Queen looks unreliable and grasping.
It's true the Knave is one of those who show
Both eyes – but set in a sneering, puffy face.
I'd rather be ruled by Spades, although the King
Seems to rely more on tradition than
His own brains for superiority;
And obviously he married far beneath him.
No doubt the Ace, unique, is the *éminence grise*.
The son, though, looks slick enough to keep the
    Spades
On top when he succeeds to that great throne.
The Hearts were always beaten by the Spades,
And quite resigned to love and pastries – she,
However, is beginning to look sour.
And then those minor royalties, the Clubs:
Despise them not – their visages are strong.
Their kingdom's poor, remote and mountainous,
But they've been known to work some clever
    coups.

One thing they share, these flowered families –
Dread of the proletarian Joker, who,
Though warning of his presence by his pallor,
Is always liable to take them by surprise.

The Art of the Possible

Ask for bunnies' ears – Notice on ice-cream van

Don't ask for automatic gears
Or Worthington's or Bass's beers
Or Scarborough or Brighton piers
Or three or even fewer cheers.

Don't ask for bandits' bandoliers
Or caliphs and their fat viziers;
Gazebos, ha-has, belvederes,
Or rapids, waterfalls and weirs.

Don't ask for eminent careers
Or universal panaceas.
Don't ask for alligators' tears
But, as you're told, for bunnies' ears.

Happy Lion

When you are really old
A mysterious lion will keep
Appearing in your dreams –
Its hide a dirty gold,
Its mane a matted heap,
Its eyes like coffee creams.

Those future dreams will prove
Deep down you've not forgotten –
That still you take to bed –
The beast you now so love:
Though then worn out its cotton,
Its stuffing long since bled.

A Memory of Kenya

The neck of an ostrich makes a J;
And though its knee-joints bend the wrong way
It travels at almost the speed of sound,
Its head and body parallel to the ground;
And its droppings are silver waterfalls
On the hot dry plains of Africa.

Bicycle Handlebars

Their shape when I was still at school
Was cows' horns, as a general rule –

Though boys whose speech was full of 'damns'
Crouched over things like horns of rams.

But now the young ride straight to hell
Bolt upright, wrestling a gazelle.

What next? Go wheeling through the dusk
Steering two tortuous mammoth's tusks?

Or at perdition's very door
Gain bovine gravity once more?

An English Explorer

An oblong trodden yellow packet on the pavement
Is not too dirty for its legend to be read,
Which is, mysteriously, 'Barratt's Sherbet
    Fountain'.
At once my thoughts to far exotic lands are led.

I see deep in the burning desert an oasis,
And there, the sudden emerald of palms among –
Perhaps a slender dancing girl or two beside it –
The sherbet fountain bubbles sherbet all day long.

And who enjoys its free and effervescent coolness
(Also enjoys the slender dancers, I suppose)?
Why, he who bravely found and named it –
    Mr Barratt –
Stretched by it, wearing khaki shorts and woollen
    hose.

Tails on Fairy Tales

1
What would the bears have done
To Goldilocks had they caught her?
Eaten her like a bun,
Or treated her like a daughter?

Someone to polish off the stodgy
Porridge, to warm the chairs,
In bed to put one's podgy
Arms round. Please come back upstairs!

2
For wolf as well as Grandma, a dreadful end.
Is there really between animals and humans
such an enmity?

Isn't it suspicious that to Red Riding Hood
the wolf spoke human language so fluently,
meeting in the wood?

It seems to me that had he been a real wolf
he'd have gone miles out of his way to avoid
a girl wearing red.

Who was he then, this villain in a wolf skin,
with such a smooth patter and an appetite?
Seen Grandpa lately?

3
When Jack chopped down the stalk
The giant was only stunned.
He lay there, white as chalk.

Jack's Ma came out, cried: 'Oh,
Here's your father back, who left me
Fifteen years ago.'

And soon he was eating pie
As heartily as in
His hide-out in the sky.

4
'Dear Cinderella,'
said the Prince one day,
'how would you like to
put on your old dress,
sit in the ashes?

'My subjects envy
our home and riches,
but now I've got you
such things don't matter:
I could give them up.'

'They matter to me,'
said Cinderella.
'You were never poor.
You never swept floors.
You could dance all night.'

'But, Cinderella,
look, the mob's raging
at the palace gates!'
'Then just arrest its
two ugly leaders.'

5
'Whoever heard of a cat
As Mayor of London? Who
Could possibly vote for you?
Besides, *I'm* a candidate.'

'Who killed all the mice and rats,
Working a twelve-hour day?
And who idles his time away?
I'm afraid, Sir Richard, there
Is a great change in the air.
Long live the working-cats!'

End of a Girl's First Tooth

Once she'd a tooth that wiggled;
Now she's a gap that lisps.
For days she could only suck lollies;
Now she champs peanuts and crithsps.

Missing Objects

Expect it's a fairy pinched my comb
To rake the garden round her home.

She's also got my ignition key –
Perhaps to lock the room where she

Keeps all a fairy's nasty things,
Like christening spells and Demon Kings.

But what (excuse the word) the hell's
She doing with my spectacles?

She can't need them to read my lost
Book, since to her the print is vast.

Besides, however could they be
Propped by a nose no bigger than a pea?

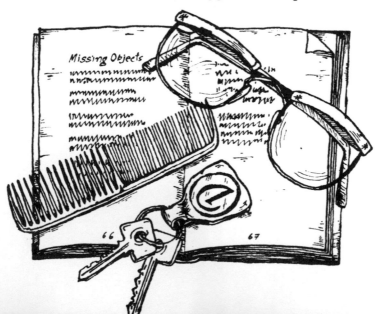

Fancy

If a thrush settles on the aerial
Can you then watch it singing on TV?
When I go in, the screen's still BBC:
Of course, the mavis could have flown off in that
    interval.

The thing is like a refrigerator light;
Or nightmares when you've wakened in the night.
Can we be sure it really is the case
That milk's in darkness and the fiend's given up
    the chase?

Meetings and Absences

How far the ships!
How wet these lips!
– Said fish to chips.

*

Don't let it ever be forgotten
Some of us thought the world was going rotten
When nasty nylon challenged cotton.

*

Nothing can really beat
For a quick sensuous treat
Clean socks on just-bathed feet.

*

A clever man called Wittgenstein maintained
If lions could speak we shouldn't understand.
A plausible remark, for ninety-nine
Out of a hundred can't grasp Wittgenstein.

       *

How does your little toe
In the bed so long and bare,
Keep on discovering
The top sheet's little tear?

       *

Ten steps down to the cellar: what a fright
To find that there are only nine tonight!

       *

Hail and farewell: that's life
– Said peas to knife.

Dinner at Blunderbore's

The giant Blunderbore,
About to dine on pork,
Called in a blunderborian roar:
'Bring me my knife and fork!'

And in four servants ran,
Trotting for dear life:
At each end of the fork one man,
And two men to the knife.

'Goodness,' one captive cried,
'This giant's awfully big.
But I'd be still more terrified
To meet a giant's pig.'

More About Blunderbore

It seems the giant Blunderbore
Is taller than a human door.
In fact, suppose him waiting to come in
All that you'd see would be a boot and shin.

But usually it's someone else
When we get up to answer bells.
And even were it actually giant B
He'd not push in much farther than his knee.

The following are the times or places
To guard against his hideous faces
(Or, more particularly, his appetite,
Which takes in children at a casual bite):

When climbing any garden tree
That's shot up rather suddenly;
Seeing a figure with a second head;
Or switching off the light to go to bed.

Insects of the Orchestra

Like a great pallid spider,
back held strangely still, scuttles
the cellist's sinister hand
up and down the finger-board.

The harpist's butterfly hands
are far too agile to get
tangled in the harp strings' web.

Some loose insects (flies perhaps)
the conductor tries to swat.

Shopping

Dearer and dearer get the things we eat
And yet today I found a shop which had
'Large Spanish navels 4 pence each': not bad
If you don't mind that cut of foreign meat.

In the Butcher's Window

How would you like *your* liver put on show
(Probably with curious knobs among the blood)?
Even your leg, all curves and white as snow,
In that position wouldn't look too good.

In the Bathroom

What is that blood-stained thing –
Hairy, as if it were frayed –
Stretching itself along
The slippery bath's steep side?

I approach it, ready to kill,
Or run away aghast;
And find I have to deal
With a used elastoplast.

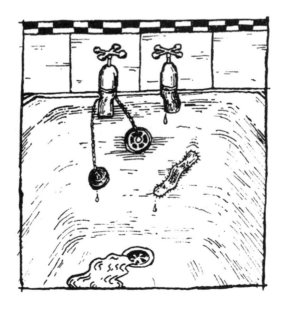

Lonely Horse

Going to Birmingham by train I saw
A horse; not grazing but his head held low.
He stood unmoving and his brown-white nose
Was rounded. In the field stood nothing else –

Except the thistle islands in the cropped
Turf; though his vision of our land was stopped
By bordering hedges. I shall think of him
Still there when I've come back from Birmingham –

Especially when I'm sitting on the lawn,
Enclosed by garden walls. If any one
Looked over them he'd see my brown and white
Moustache and head bent downwards as I write.

Household Riddles

I sing – I'm not the tranny.
I'm 'on', though not TV.
Like interfering Grannie
I help to make the tea.

*

'Full, over-full, is my heart:
Please take me away.'
'We'll send a dirty cart
Every week. OK?'

*

Whatever colour I may be
I smother you with white.
Afterwards, all (especially
Your nose) is shining bright.

*

You can tell how wound up I am:
I can't even say 'Oh damn!'
Just stutter, and point all round
With a slightly trembling hand.

*

Even strangers succumb
At once to my charms.
They sink in my arms
As I'm pressing their bum.

*

No wonder the face is deathly white:
One nostril's got a streaming cold.
Wise to be gargling – may hold up
Infection spreading to the throat.

*

Is it a worm-cast or a worm?
I think the latter would be more firm.
But whoever heard of a worm's footprint
Tasting so strongly of peppermint?

*

Round and round I go,
Moderately fast or rather slow,
But no one watches me:
It's song not dance comes from my circularity.

*

My ear's as black as night
(My mouth's black, too).
I've brothers who are white
But they are rather few.
(I should add: it's my mouth through which I hear
And therefore have to whisper with my ear.)

Fruit Dish

Like babies, the apple has a dimpled bottom –
Which lets it sit securely on a dish;
Without its little stalk it's able also
To sit down on its top half. Cleverish!

But even if it had a top-half dimple
A pear would be top-heavy on its top.
The globose peach must try to get some comfort
In plastic dimples in the fruiterer's shop.

When ovoid grapes are parted from their fellows
It's almost certain they'll roll far and wide.
How curious that, like a human, bandy
Bananas safely slumber on their side!

Gentleman Standing on the Street

Definitely not a good figure:
His waist could hardly be bigger.
From bottom to rather flat head
His complexion is horribly red.
Under a small white moustache
The mouth is a wide open gash.
He wears his initials below
But his actual name I don't know –
Everard Rolypoly
The Second? He'd make a fine goalie.

I see from the figures enclosed
In his vest that I've missed the last post.

'Be a Monster'

I am a frightful monster,
My face is cabbage green
And even with my mouth shut
My teeth can still be seen.
My finger-nails are like rats' tails
And very far from clean.

I cannot speak a language
But make a wailing sound.
It could be any corner
You find me coming round.
Then, arms outspread and eyeballs red,
I skim across the ground.

The girls scream out and scatter
From this girl-eating bat.
I usually catch a small one
Because her legs are fat;
Or it may be she's tricked by me
Wearing her grandpa's hat.

Macbeth

'Fillet of a fenny snake,
In the cauldron boil and bake.'
Did the witch intend to say
Boil the liquid quite away,
And go on applying heat
Till the thing is fit to eat?
Then, why not put in that skillet
All the snake not just the fillet?
Which is worse, the poetry
Or the careless recipe?

*

Who would imagine making salad were
At all to do with poetry and death?
And yet what peeled and cut the beetroot are
The guilty frightening fingers of Macbeth.

*

'Light thickens; and the crow
Makes wings to th' rooky wood.'
Nobody seems to know
If the lines are bad or good.
Some think in those few words
Are too many darkling birds.
But it must have marred the book
Had Shakespeare said 'the rook
Makes wings to th' crowy wood.'

A Portrait of the Author

How unmemorable to meet Mr Fuller
With his eyes of piercing blue,
His talk getting duller and duller,
His eyes piercing all except you!

Was he, then, ever worth meeting,
Perhaps in his far-off youth?
No, after his amiable greeting
He soon appeared somewhat uncouth.

He has managed to carry on singing
In a voice rather trembly and harsh,
Like a rook that goes garglingly winging
Over rubbish dump, factory and marsh.

He hopes that the world will be thumbing
His works when he's no longer there.
What a hope, when those seeing him coming
Cross the street with a ruminant air!

There leap on his lap feline friskers
And assume a leonine pose;
Babies meditate over his whiskers
And pull his unaquiline nose.

But only a few adults mutter:
'We must have old Fuller to dine.
We might get him actually to utter
If we ply him with plenty of wine.'

The Ageing Poet Sees a Sinister Being

A motor waiting by the library.
On the back seat a man with curly hair –
Wild hair, long nose. Strange man. Impatient air.

I guess the driver's in the library,
Possibly asking for a book that gives
Advice on restless long-nosed relatives;
Or even looking up the address of some
Convenient loony-bin. And now I come
Nearer the car I see that it's high time
Something was done about this man of crime:
He's actually collared like a dog, no doubt
To slip a chain through when they take him out.

'Like a dog?' As I pass the car, the light
Of truth dawns on my poor old brain and sight.

A Cumberland Couple

There was an old man of Kesique
Who was terribly fond of bezique;
Which goes to explain
Why in humorous vein
He usually called Keswick Kesique.

There was an old woman of Keswick –
Bezique she referred to as bezwick,
No doubt to amuse
Or annoy or confuse
Her husband, who rarely said Keswick.

On the Heath

Seagulls and rooks at rest
On Blackheath might bequeath
The name (if re-named now)
Of Blackandwhiteyheath.

*

In all the years I've gone across the heath
This morning is the first time that I've seen
In use the Metropolitan Drinking Fountain
And Cattle Trough Association's trough.
After the climb from Greenwich a little horse
Has stopped, and drinks, then pulls its cart
    among
The silly motor cars towards Shooters Hill
On legs as gravity-defyingly gay
(Yet sad) as in Victoria's trough-providing day.

*

Hands deep in the pockets of my short black
    raincoat,
Trailing umbrella hooked around my forearm,
I pass a rook who makes as though to fly up,
    Then looks again and settles.

I expect it thought at first: here comes a human.
Then with a double-take it recognized an
Enormous (and unfortunately one-winged)
    But indubitable brother.

*

A really rather clever sculptor made
A body for the gulls.
Pity a child's pen was allowed to add,
For legs, two verticals.

But on the pond these uprights disappear –
Gulls look like little swans.
In red lacquer leggings, pigeons watch on shore
With envious eyes of bronze.

*

The apex of a parish boundary stump looks not
Like iron but an obelisk of sardonyx –
Polished by children's pants
Since 1896.

*

A motor-mower plays the great
Green record of the heath and leaves
Debris-filled grooves on which the stares
Descend like black-cloaked thieves.

Making a noise like aerosols,
A young stare, dark-eyed as a gypsy,
Staggers behind its parents as
Though it were rather tipsy.

I'm going home to lunch and think
How little I'd look forward to
Larvae and worms – uncooked at that –
For which the starlings queue.

Seven Flies

Each autumn in the kitchen
A fly remains. The same?
How can we tell? Except
It seems to grow more tame.

*

If you're a house-fly
Then I wonder why
You bang on the glass
That keeps you from grass.

*

You know by my flapping hand I hate your flight;
So why do you want to kiss me in the night?

*

Fly, who's been very naughty on my dough-
Nut, why do I push the window, let you go?

*

Fly in the milk, I spoon you out alive
And grieve you're too bedraggled to survive.

*

Still fly against the wall – it is as if
I stood asleep upon an upright cliff.

*

A fly on the kitchen pane –
Surely that fly of old!
With cunning suddenness
I push the window out
And as quickly shut it again;

The fly still on the glass
But on the outside now.
Unmoving, sulking, it stays,
Its diamond eyes upon
Sugar and cake and him
Who plays dirty tricks on flies.

Setting up a Bird-Table

I thought I should attract goldcrests,
Goldfinches, eagles, wigeons;
And knots and bonxies from their nests;
The nervous goldeneye.
But all I did was multiply
The sparrows and the pigeons.

Manna

It's raining bread,
Like the Bible said.

What I just threw
Was seized by a few
Sparrows, with greed;
And now they feed
On the high boughs
Or roof of the house.
But manna spills
From little bills,
Juggling not too well.
And straightway drops
In the great crops
Of the pigeons of Israel.

Dog Days

I know what the dogs are feeling
Tied up to the 'Doggy Bar'
By the doors of the supermarket
Where their lords and mistresses are;
So near yet (for dogs) so far.

Noses are pointed shopwards,
Legs twitch in a nervous dance,
Tails are unrolled with anguish;
A grudging brown-eyed glance
Rates my significance.

Ears scarcely turn as I utter
What's meant as a kindly word;
All the more kind since my shoe was
Only this afternoon spurred
(As it were) by a doggy turd.

The Bad Samaritan

On the way home I see in the road ahead
A black thing, stirring slightly. Cat or bird,
Hit by a car, in need of help; yet I'm
Afraid to find it hurt beyond my power,
Needing a *coup-de-grâce* I couldn't bear
To give. And so turn off and reach my house
A devious way by which I manage to
Get out of passing the catastrophe.
That's how too-tender hearts to cowardice
Are led.
            And waking in the night at three
I think about suffering and my neglect,
That after all I might have saved a life;
Though soon the usual imaginings
About the future of my own affairs
Charm me to sleep again.
                   Next day I go
On grave business to the Bank and GPO,
Speak to a neighbour shaving privet, emerge
Into the traffic. In the gutter, squashed,
A dark felt hat that flutters; quite dead, though:
Memory of pain, and undeserved relief!
Would that all sin could end in happiness
(I think), and add to my iniquities.

September Songs

So you're one of the Embers. By Jove,
Wonders will never cease!
You're *far* less dark than Nov
And *not* like that cold fish, Dec.

*

The moon seems far away tonight
And yet unusually bright.
It made me sure I'd carelessly
Left on the outside front-door light.
That's how I came to meet its eye.

*

What should an old man do beneath this sky
Of azure pottery?

Sit by the sedum and hope a butterfly
Will light on it or me.

What happens is a black thing flying by
Falls in my cup of tea.

Nasty Night

Whose are the hands you hear
Pulling the roof apart?
What stamps its hoof
Between the bedroom ceiling and the slates?

Nice Day

What's happened to the fear
That all night wrung your heart?
Who's mended the roof
So pigeons may bow and twirl before their mates?

The Dark

I feared the darkness as a boy;
And if at night I had to go
Upstairs alone I'd make a show
Of carrying on with those below
A dialogue of shouts and 'whats?'
So they'd be sure to save poor Roy
Were he attacked by vampire bats.

Or thugs or ghosts. But far less crude
Than criminal or even ghost
Behind a curtain or a post
Was what I used to dread the most –
The always-unseen bugaboo
Of black-surrounded solitude.
I dread it still at sixty-two.

Literature at Dead of Night

As I lie and read in bed
A spider spins above my head.
Rising from my lamp, the air
Agitates the spider's lair.
This and my story make me feel
That I'm fictional, not real –
Miss Havisham in *David Copp-
erfield*, perhaps. The hailstones drop
Against the window like the nights
More usual at Wuthering Heights.

Up and down the staircase go
Characters from E. A. Poe.

The Game of Life

Have you been in sight of heaven
Far ahead on ninety-seven,
Then swirled the dice and thrown a one,
Slid down a snake and flopped upon
Some square like sixty-three?

And then what made you even madder
Seen your sister climb a ladder
To eighty-four from twenty-eight
And felt a sudden rush of hate
As she smirked with glee?

And have you thought she counted out
(So as to miss a snake's dread snout)
A few too many squares – and stayed
Quiet because you were afraid
Or just through leniency?

If so, you will already know
How bitter life can be; and show
Upon your countenance no sign
Except perhaps a smile benign.
And shake on doggedly.

The Poet: As Typist

When with two fingers I am typing out
A work of mine, instead of 'poetry'
'Pottery' sometimes comes or 'potery'.

Pottery must make the reader doubt:
Can Fuller here be talking sensibly,
For once, of cup and saucer, lid and spout?

Potery's just as mad as poetry.

The Poet: His Public

I wrote a book for girls and boys –
Seen Grandpa Lately?
I doubt if any child enjoys
It greatly.

But several grown-ups said to me:
'It's rather good –
The first lot of your poetry
We've understood.'

The Poet: His Reward

In a quaint shop I found a pot of Delf,
Almost as old as Ghibelline and Guelph.

I took the lid off – there stepped out an elf
Who, pleased at being rescued, gave me pelf.

How lucky to have reached up to that shelf!
A poet's always short of . . . rhymes for 'self'.

On the River Cherwell

Lying in a punt you get
A swan's-eye view of all the wet
Gliding by, long jerk by jerk,
As though webs were in fact at work.

Your bare arm, languid as a neck,
Droops down as if it meant to peck
Some passing weed, and idly lingers,
Cold running through its beak of fingers.

Elijah's Thanks

God said to Elijah 'I've
Told ravens that you must be fed.'
So the birds kept him alive
With flesh and bread.

Who told later humans that
It was birds that should be fed?
On lawns lie biblical lamb fat
And friendly bread.

After Apollo

At least the sky's not spoiled by man.
I look up from the whizzing street,
The treeless pavement, shuffling feet,
And see the star-points' ancient plan.

The universe has let us know
Only a single mystic face;
Which even now bears not a trace
Of boot or shovel on its glow.

Tree Houses

Orang-outangs, small beasts
Nearest to humans! Nomads,
Nightly you build new nests.

Five thousand of you only
Remain. Tree houses make
Night hours less mad and lonely.

How lucky, we, your cousins,
Here, now – who back in time
Were counted, too, in dozens!

Our children merely play
At living in the trees
And then just during day;

Although, if history grows
Worse, we may have to quit
Cities and take to boughs –

Where windows, walls and doors
Are mended by Spring, which also
Crowns them with higher floors.

A Girl's Girl Friend

It's really a shame
Time went by
Before we became
Friends till we die.

Your three terms in the Lower Fourth
Might have been in the frozen north.
Now it seems even more absurd
My being lonely in the Third.

How queer it is you also felt
Miss Pink too thick to wear a belt;
And gazed at Mrs Brown's moustache
And thought her view of Robespierre harsh!

And were you really that old geezer
Who carefully fell in *Julius Caesar*?
I blush to think you heard me play
Fluffs in the *Polonaise in A*.

Now we shall sit together on
Trips to the mammoth's skeleton
Or a verse reading by Ted Hughes,
Giggling as though we'd low IQs.

And when we go to see *Sylphides*
Or study surds or *Adam Bede*
We'll keep in titters though such things
Aren't wholly apt for titterings.

And shall we share the glittering prizes
Or drop out somewhere near Devizes?
I think I'd bet my bottom dollar
You'd try to deviate me from squalor.

Let's swear to see
Only the funny side
And sadness be
The mood we hide.

Let's hinder hurt
Spreading about.
Let's wear each other's shirts
Till they wear out.

Leaving School

Our Blackheath Comprehensive School (for mice)
Provides a master who will give advice
About careers; and if he's not a fool,
In his last term, or earlier, at school
A mouse should see his master on the tricky
Problem of work. His name is Mr Michie.
His desk is covered with brochures on what
Sheer fun it is to join the Army, not
A cat in sight, while you, sent overseas,
Chat up the local ladies over cheese;
On openings in Town (where jobs abound
And even humans travel underground).
Perhaps the most attractive are the places
Where the top portion of the human race is –
Those vacancies for clearing up the bits
In the vast kitchens of the Hotel Ritz
Or the Elysium of the hungry mouse –
After a garden party at Buck House,
Where every woman (also every man)
Leave their Swiss Rolls to gawp at Princess Anne.
Of course, few rodents have the *savoir faire*
To keep up with the social standards there –
Not to neglect to bow, say, to the Prince,
Hiding your tart of strawberry jam or mince.
So Michie, talking to a rather hairy
School-leaver called (you might have guessed it)
   Gary,
Advised against the Piccadilly scene
And also lodging with HM the Queen.

'Gary,' he said, 'I'd like to see you try
For something in science or technology.
One of the Defence Establishments, perhaps,
Working on antidotes and anti-traps.'

'Oh no, sir. Such things aren't for me. I've
    planned
To tour the world with what you'd call my "band" –
In fact, a group known as "The Bacon Rind".'

'Ah Gary, I'm afraid you're just as blind
As those Three of our species in the rhyme.
At least a million young mice at this time
Aspire to make a journey to the stars
By beating drums or strumming on guitars.
And all they do is prove what people say –
"As noisy as a mouse". Mice shouldn't play
If the (rock) cats are going to stay away.'

'Oh very clever, sir. But we're a lot
Already booked for TV's cultural spot.
Fame among highbrows will be in the bag,
After we're introduced by Melvyn Bragg.'

Collecting

I wonder what will happen to the stills from *War
  and Peace*;
Old bottles that held ginger-beer, old jars cosmetic
  grease;

The stamps commemorating curious recent history –
Winston's peaked cap or half a century of the BBC;

The grisly shelves of Conan Doyle, ram's horns
  and avian skulls;
The discs (that anyway you sing by heart) of
  musicals;

To André Previn, Susan Hampshire, Valerie
  Singleton,
Whose mugs or autographs unarguably at the
  moment stun

Those entering your room (despite the warning on
  the door)
And stepping round the racket and the flute-case
  on the floor.

Whatever in the end may be these childhood
  relics' doom –
Dustbin or safe-deposit or museum's Fuller room –

They will return some day: your ancient heart will
   throb again
For stout Pierre, or mortal sheep in Celtic summer
   rain.

But strange that things held precious may well
   vanish God knows where –
As in the case of pearly baby-teeth and long gold
   hair.

Human and Canine Race

I often say I only need to go
To shops a hundred yards or so away
For something to enrich a humdrum day.

This morning I met father, son and dog.
They had been playing with a football on
The heath: old dog, young father, infant son.

No doubt they were going home. The child was last,
The father next, the dog (though short on strength,
Cataracts in both its eyes) led by a length.

Hogs

'Erratic and eccentric in every way' –
Says Dr Burton in his book* about
The hedgehog. In hibernation its ears, toes, snout
Are as cold as if the animal were dead.
Its spiny evolution has made it blasé;
But rolling up, though disconcerting dogs,
Cannot protect pedestrian hogs from road-hogs.

'Dimwitted' – yet a hog called Martha won't
Come if her master calls out 'Martin'. Don't
(Should you have a hog as pet) trouble to buy
Anything special for tea – though it prefers
Tinned salmon, it will deign to eat an egg
Yolk lightly boiled. Frustrated, its behaviour
Is like an infant in a tantrum. Eye
Feeble but large; a terrier's wet nose
For sniffing. New-born offspring of the hog
Resemble, as once I noticed, speckled baps:
Alas, these had, eccentrically perhaps,
Decided they would hibernate for ever.

*The Hedgehog: by Maurice Burton

In the Future

Is it only in our dreaming
That we come across a garden,
Vapour pouring from a bonfire,
In the bed a slanted shovel,
But no gardener stooping, stretching;
At the pathway's end, a doorway
Open to a homely kitchen;
No one eating at the table
Though a place is set; a mongrel
Fast asleep upon the hearth-rug?

Yet it's certain in the future
Someone really will discover
Smoking leaves and smoking sausage,
Dog with ears for our steps only –
And enjoy the things we planted.

Which as they appear will surely
(As they do for us who planted!),
Like new poets in their decades,
With their genius astonish.

If ourselves should then be dreaming
It might be of empty gardens.

Grandfather to Milkman

A DOZEN EGGS, PLEASE. There are three
Attractive females due for tea.

More than most food eggs are preferred.
Would *I* were some girl-pleasing bird!

Inscrutable Features

Walking along,
My right big-toe seemed wrong.
When I took off my shoe
I saw a head peeping through.

Quite a shock:
A midget in my sock,
With flattish, yellowish face –
Perhaps of the Chinese race.

Outside the Greengrocer's

What an odd place for these mad fans to gather
(Actually on the pavement) and play their games.
I nearly knock them over. Curious, too, such
Brains should be found in small brown craniums.
– Although I feel it was a weakness, rather,
For them to label themselves so largely 'CHESSNUTS'.

In the Public Library

The infant, while his mother peers at novels,
Sings of a black sheep and its cry and fleece.
She doesn't seem to worry that he grovels
In mucky footprints and the parquet's grease.

I have to step across the raucous singer
(Anorak making him still more obese.)
I could, but don't, tread on his grubby finger;
Though let him see my face – a cruel crook's.

I only hope his life will gain from books.

Waiting for the Prince

When the Bad Fairy cast her spell
And all at once the palace fell
   Asleep, there was a roamer
   Still, through the general coma.

Magic's not worth a row of beans
For insomnia, and so the Queen's
   Old father wandered, bored,
   While all the others snored.

He saw moustaches wave like fronds
Disturbed by tiny fish in ponds;
   And what so often drips
   In sleep from open lips.

Only the nightwatchman was in bed –
Pyjamas striped in green and red:
   His bedside clock would ring
   In vain that evening.

Some were stuck in places highly
Awkward for sleep – a groom called Reilly,
   For instance, far from view
   In a dark outside loo.

And stablehands lay down with mares,
Milkmaids with cows, jesters with bears,
   And in an awful mess
   Slumbered the young Princess.

Around her, paperbacks, cassettes,
A sweater, a tennis racket, pets –
   A kitten, a cockatoo –
   Used tissues, quite a few.

Like a bag of bits of string, her hair;
Her toes not over-clean, and bare.
   Her grandfather, passing by,
   Let out a pitying sigh;

And put things in drawers and her to bed –
Because you never know (he said)
   Soon someone else who cares
   May catch her unawares.

A Peculiar Christmas

Snow? Absolutely not.
In fact, the weather's quite hot.
At night you can watch this new
Star without catching the 'flu.

Presents? Well, only three.
But then there happen to be
Only three guests. No bells,
No robins, no fir-trees, no smells

– I mean of roast turkey and such:
There are whiffs in the air (a bit much!)
Of beer from the near public house,
And of dirty old shepherds, and cows.

The family party's rather
Small – baby, mother and father –
Uncles, aunts, cousins dispersed.
Well, this Christmas *is* only the first.

Christmas Day

Small girls on trikes
Bigger on bikes
Collars on tykes

Looking like cads
Patterned in plaids
Scarf-wearing dads

Chewing a choc
Mum in a frock
Watches the clock

Knocking in pans
Fetching of Grans
Gathering of clans

Hissing from tins
Sherries and gins
Upping of chins

Corks making pops
'Just a few drops'
Watering of chops

All this odd joy
Tears at a broken toy
Just for the birth long ago of a boy

Autumn Mornings

I rush into the garden with a cry:
The intruder, cheekily slow, prepares to flee.
First it's the next-door cat with bird-filled eye.
I rush into the garden. With a cry
Of protest, Tompkins (as he's called) slinks by.
Then it's a squirrel in my walnut tree –
I rush into the garden with a cry.
The intruder cheekily slow. Prepares to flee?

More About Tompkins

One evening Tompkins' 'Mummy' calls –
  Lady two doors away.
Have we seen Tompkins anywhere?
  – Missing for all that day,
  Yet never known to stray.

Always most punctual for his meals
  And, if abroad at night,
Letting himself into the house
  Usually by earliest light;
  And never known to fight.

His Mummy looks me in the eye
  And sees into my mind.
She says, of course he's now too old
  To catch the avian kind –
  Too slow, perhaps too blind.

She knows (in fact, she tells me that
  She lately read the same)
I wrote a verse about her cat –
  His cruel, sneaky game –
  Mentioning him by name.

By 'game' I mean his creeping through
  The shrubs on slow-motion paws,
Low as a snake, to pounce upon
  Sparrows and doves and daws
  With murderous teeth and claws.

I shout at him, I clap my hands,
　　Whenever he's around.
He still seems capable to me
　　Of making a sudden bound,
　　Causing a mortal wound.

I say: 'I saw him yesterday' –
　　Don't add that probably
He chattered at me from the wall
　　(Spying the enemy
　　Who foils his villainy)

And that I gnash my teeth at *him*.
　　Then, I'd been gardening, thus
The shed-door was ajar. So now
　　Feeling ridiculous,
　　I open it, call out: 'Puss!'

His Mummy adds in her own tones
　　Words much more intimate.
I see among the rakes and spades
　　An old soft trilby hat,
　　Nothing else like a cat.

I never had the car out, so
　　No point in looking where
My Daimler lives – an object which,
　　Like Tompkins, doth (I fear)
　　Oft in my verse appear.

Scarcely had Tompkins' Mummy gone,
    When back she came. And said
She'd been inspired by me to look
    In her own garden-shed,
    And the given-up-for-dead –

Tompkins, no less – had run out, cross,
    Straight to his waiting food;
Typically, stopping not to give
    Thanks to some clever god
    For this miraculous good.

'He'd been in there all night and day' –
    Bright was his Mummy's eye.
Strangely, a lump came in my throat
For one who used to get my goat.
    In future, then, will my
    Foes frolic freely by?

Further Verses for the Cat Tomkins

Two moggies play a noisy feline game
And wake me in the night. I think of thee.
It seems I made an error with the name:
Tomkins, not Tompkins, was your owner's choice –
After the old composer, Thomas T;
She obviously not considering your voice.

Characters

Sparrows wait on the garden seat for crumbs.
Their rather few toes rattle on the wood,
Not like the pigeon's, red as blood, but pale
As mine. Are those two at the back called thumbs?

Their beaks proportionately seem as big
As toucans'. They sit legless on their tails,
But I can see their mandarins' nails stretched out;
Head-feathers untidy as a clever wig.

There are as many in the world as us:
Each one that riffles the air in landing here
Presents a character as clear as those
Of humankind I see wait for a bus.

In the Garden

Out of the bird-bath, I
Lift up a shapeless struggling, and
See it on my finger-end
Change to a tiny fly.

What great things can be done
By love; and patient polishing,
With several legs, of face and wing –
Even a life re-won!

Beyond the Window

Not far beyond the window is a tree
Webbing the four o'clock December sky.
If humans were the only things alive
And that had always been so on our star,
Of course I should be terrified to see
(As I do now) a blackbird leap along
The boughs, and thread the twigs, and thus
    mount high –
So heavy-seeming and so purposive,
Active so near the coming of the night.
I sit and watch it, clutching my mug of tea,
Until the tea is chilly on the tongue.
Familiar with lesser creatures though we are,
I do, I must say, feel a little fright;
As though it were a rat looked down on me.

How to Boil an Egg (and Eat it)

To save fuel bills, get
the water from the hot
tap, using a small pan.
Then puncture with a pin
(not the little end
but the big) to expand
shell-cracking air inside
the egg when it's lowered
into the water. How
long boiling to allow
each must decide (and rate
some eggs' eccentric weight)
but I'd tell a daughter
four and a short quarter.

Though starting as an egg,
what (perching on one leg)
faces me now is some
bald man or tubby gnome.
Are you supposed to eat
him, or interrogate?

Avoid an haemorrhage
of nourishing gamboge
by slicing off the dome
less blunted; and consume
with bread, butter, sea salt
and white pepper, exult-
ing in nature's bounty.
As to hen husbandry,
putting quite out of mind
its outrage to the kind.

Who?

Who dresses in rags, though could be rich;
And may sleep sometimes in a ditch?
Whose hands and face are grained with pitch,
And has a hooked and running snitch,
And very often seems to itch?
Who owns a black-coated, red-eyed bitch,
And yet from hag to cat may switch?
Who makes your hair rise up and twitch,
Standing unmoving in a niche?
Who dances round without a stitch?
Whose grandad cured the Czarevitch?
– Madam Malibran, the witch.

School in the Holidays

The empty playground quivers,
   Still stand the summer trees;
From maps long, wriggling rivers
   White mountains, azure seas,

Look down on empty places
   And polished, silent floors.
Tanned are the absent faces,
   Unslammed the classroom doors.

What ghost has left a cycle
   Propped in the shadowed shed?
Can Gary, Bill or Michael
   Be numbered with the dead?

The Ballad of Boggarthole Clough

In grimy old Manchester town was I born,
And in my boyhood 'twas pleasure enough
To bicycle out on a high summer morn
And picnic at Boggarthole Clough.
For Boggarthole Clough, in spite of its name,
Was a countrified place of picnicking fame –
No boggarts in Boggarthole Clough.

It was there, rather older, I met the fair maid
Whose dress was of thin summer stuff,
Whose cool hand I took as we walked through the
   glade
And the vale that were Boggarthole Clough.
At Boggarthole Clough, every subsequent year,
I expected to see that delectable dear,
The fair maid of Boggarthole Clough.

But only a very few summers had gone
And my visits to Boggarthole Clough
Quite simply consisted of wand'rings alone
Through the undergrowth, gloomy and rough,
Searching for one I'd imagined was mine,
Who had given to me not a word nor a sign
Of departing from Boggarthole Clough.

Now, many years past, there are houses that stand
In the fields, on the slopes, by the bluff,
Still called (although utterly changed from the land
Of my boyhood) Boggarthole Clough.
And I saw myself there and the one that was fair,
As dumb now as ever we formerly were –
The boggarts of Boggarthole Clough.

Another Portrait of the Author

Professor Fuller seems to be
   A most impressive man.
He lectures upon poetry,
His hair is brushed, his nose is free
From smuts, he drives an azure V-
   8 Daimler, not a van.

Sometimes he ventilates his views
   In a decided way:
More often he is seen to muse,
Gazing at clouds or on his shoes;
All wait in vain for him to choose
   What he is going to say.

The truth is really that behind
   The professorial brow
There is a very simple mind
Thinking of crispy bacon rind,
How Charlton Athletic have declined,
   Not When and Why and How.

He's just as foolish now as when
   Some umpteen years ago
He only knew his twice and ten
Times tables, and his feeble pen
Wrote 'sieze' and 'mischevious' and then
   Blots like a domino.